CHEESE
HOLIDAYS

G000254687

Postcard

Wallace & Gromit

Postcard

Wallace & Gromit

'No cheese, Gromit!'
From *A Grand Day Out* © 1989 NFTS

Postcard

Electronics for Dogs
From *A Grand Day Out* © 1989 NFTS

Postcard

Space research and construction
workshop, 62 West Wallaby St.
From *A Grand Day Out* © 1989 NFTS

Postcard

Putting on the finishing touches

From *A Grand Day Out* © 1989 NFTS

Postcard

'Sixty seconds to blast-off . . .'
From *A Grand Day Out* © 1989 NFTS

Postcard

Wallace & Gromit

Experiments with
gravity and weightlessness
From *A Grand Day Out* © 1989 NFTS

Postcard

'Cheddar . . . ? Camembert . . . ?'
From *A Grand Day Out* © 1989 NFTS

The Wallace and Gromit Postcard Book © 1993
BBC Children's Books, a division of BBC Enterprises Ltd

Postcard

'Set co-ordinates for
62 West Wallaby Street.'

From *A Grand Day Out* © 1989 NFTS

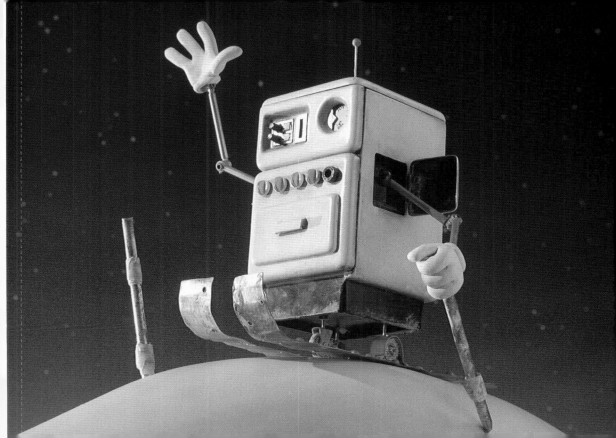

Postcard

Is there life on the moon?
From *A Grand Day Out* © 1989 NFTS

Postcard

Tea and toast

From *The Wrong Trousers*
© 1993 Wallace and Gromit Ltd

Postcard

'They're techno trousers, ex-NASA.
I think you'll find these a valuable
addition to our modern lifestyle.'

From *The Wrong Trousers*
© 1993 Wallace and Gromit Ltd

Postcard

'It's no use. We'll have
to let out the spare room.'

From *The Wrong Trousers*
© 1993 Wallace and Gromit Ltd

Postcard

The lodger arrives

From *The Wrong Trousers*
© 1993 Wallace and Gromit Ltd

Postcard

Feathers McGraw settles in

From *The Wrong Trousers*
© 1993 Wallace and Gromit Ltd

Postcard

'Don't panic!
Everything's under control.'

From *The Wrong Trousers*
© 1993 Wallace and Gromit Ltd